Dear Parent,

The My First Steps to Reading® series is based on a teaching activity that helps children learn to recognize letters and their sounds. The use of predictable language patterns and repetition of familiar words will also help your child build a basic sight vocabulary. Your child will enjoy watching the characters in the books place imaginative objects in "letter boxes." You and your child can even create and fill your own letter box, using stuffed animals, cut-out pictures, or other objects beginning with the same letter. The things you can do together are limited only by your imagination. Learning letters will be fun—the first important step on the road to reading.

The Editors

My "b" Book

(Blends are included in this book.)

written by Jane Belk Moncure

illustrated by Colin King

Little had a box.

"I will find things that begin with my 'b' sound," she said.

"I will put them into
my sound box."

Little b put on her bonnet
and went for a walk.

Little **b** found a bird

and a birdbath.

Did she put the bird and the birdbath
into her box?

She did.

Little b found a bunny.

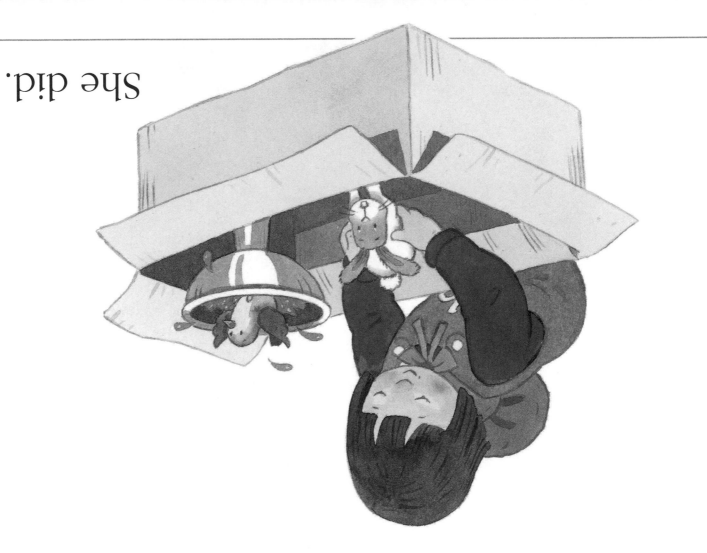

Did she put the bunny into her box
with the bird and the birdbath?

She did.

Then Little **b** heard a sound,

"bzzzz," It was a bee.

She put the bee into her box . . .

carefully!

Next, she found a

baby baboon

in a tree.

The baby baboon
was eating a banana.

"I will put you into my box,"
said Little b.

The box was so big she
could hardly carry it.

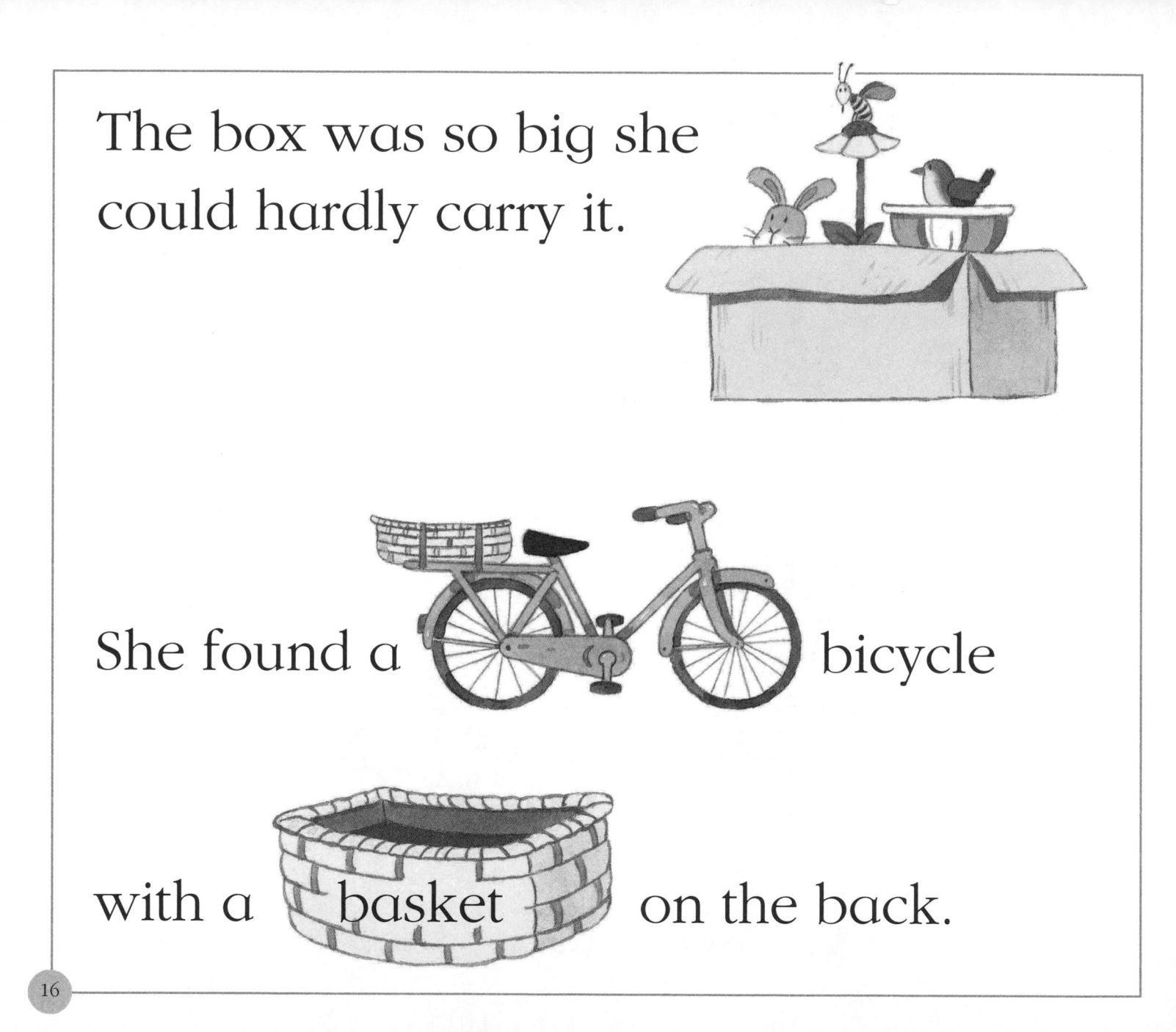

She found a bicycle

with a basket on the back.

She put the  box

into the basket

and rode the bicycle

over a big bump!

The baby baboon,

the bunny,

and the bird

bounced out of the box.

And Little b bounced off the bicycle.

"That was a bad bump," she said.

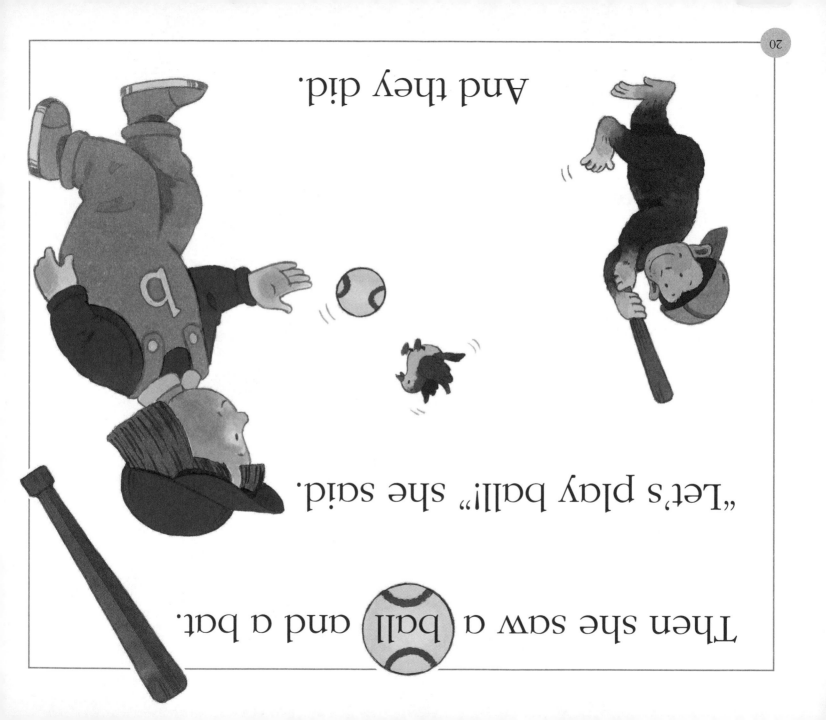

And they did.

"Let's play ball!" she said.

Then she saw a ball and a bat.

The baby baboon
hit the ball with the bat.

It bounced
into a bush.

Something was behind the bush.

It was a bear.

The bear

gave the ball to Little b.

"Thank you," she said.

She put the bear, the bush, and the ball into her box. She put the baby baboon, the bat, the bird, the birdbath, and the bunny back, too.

The bee said, "*Buzz, buzz,* this box may break."

"I must find something bigger,"

said Little b.

She rode her
bicycle over a

bridge.

Under the bridge, she saw a big, big boat. She jumped into the boat and took the things out of her box. "This is big enough," she said, "big enough for all of us."

And it was!

Can you read these words

with Little b?

balloon

barn

bell

butterfly

block

bowl

bone

bed

book

belt

boots

"Bye-bye!"

Aa Bb Cc Dd Ee Ff
Nn Oo Pp Qq Rr Ss Tt

My First Steps to READING®

ROBERT H. BECK

HAROLD C. DEUTSCH

PHILIP M. RAUP

ARNOLD M. ROSE

JOHN G. TURNBULL

assisted by JEAN BELDEN TABER

The Changing Structure of Europe

ECONOMIC, SOCIAL, AND POLITICAL TRENDS

UNIVERSITY OF MINNESOTA PRESS · MINNEAPOLIS

Library of Congress Catalog Card Number: 73-110659

ISBN 0-8166-0566-1